Dennis
and the
Big Decisions

Paul Sambrooks
Illustrated by Tommaso Levente Tani

Published by
British Association for Adoption & Fostering
(BAAF)
Saffron House
6-10 Kirby Street
London EC1N 8TS
www.baaf.org.uk

Charity registration 275689 (England and Wales)
and SC039337 (Scotland)

British Library Cataloguing in Publication Data
A catalogue record for this book is available
from the British Library

ISBN 978 1 907585 17 3

Designed and typeset by Helen Joubert Design
Printed in Great Britain by The Lavenham Press
Trade distribution by Turnaround Publisher Services, Unit 3,
Olympia Trading Estate, Coburg Road, London N22 6TZ

BAAF is the leading UK-wide membership organisation for all
those concerned with adoption, fostering and child care issues.

The author

Paul Sambrooks qualified as a social worker in 1991 and has experience in a variety of social work settings. Since 1996, he has represented the interests of children in family courts, in both public and private law matters. He was employed by The Children's Society until 2002 when he joined the Children and Family Court Advisory and Support Service (CAFCASS).

The illustrator

Tommaso Levente Tani is a picture book illustrator and has illustrated *The Teazles' Baby Bunny*, *Finding a Family for Tommy* and *Dennis Duckling*, all published by BAAF (www.leventetani.com).

This publication has been generously supported by The Stanley Smith General Charitable Trust.

Once upon a time, there was a little duckling called Dennis who lived with his mum and dad and little sister on a pond. His mum and dad couldn't look after Dennis and his little sister. So a grown-up duck called Annie took them to live with a family of ducks who lived on a river.

3

After a while Dennis and his little sister liked the duck family and they got used to living on the river. But they wanted to see their mum and dad and they missed their pond.

Dennis and his sister wanted to know if they could go home and who would look after them.

'What's going to happen?' asked Dennis.

Dennis's mum and dad and Annie had to think hard about what would be best for Dennis and his little sister. All the grown-up ducks knew they had big decisions to make...

Where should Dennis and his little sister live? Who should look after them? Who should visit them?

Annie thought they should ask a clever Owl to help them decide. So they all went to the woods to talk to the clever Owl who listened very carefully.

The clever Owl wanted to know what Dennis and his little sister thought and how they felt. So the clever Owl asked a helpful pigeon to go and talk to them.

The helpful pigeon came to see Dennis and his little sister to find out what they thought and how they felt. She also talked to Dennis's mum and dad, to Annie, and to the ducks who were looking after Dennis and his little sister.

The helpful pigeon now knew what Dennis and his little sister, and their mum and dad, and Annie, and the ducks who were looking after them wanted to happen. But not everyone wanted the same thing! So the pigeon and the grown-up ducks went to talk to the clever Owl again.

The clever Owl listened carefully to what everyone wanted to say. The helpful pigeon explained what Dennis and his little sister thought and how they felt.

The clever Owl thought very hard about what would be best for Dennis and his little sister.

11

Should Dennis and his little sister go back to their mum and dad on the pond? Would their mum and dad be able to look after them?

Or should Dennis and his little sister stay with the ducks on the river? How long would they be able to stay there? Would their mum and dad be able to visit them?

Or should Annie find a new mum and dad for Dennis and his little sister? How would the ducklings feel about having a new forever mum and dad?

After lots of thinking, the clever Owl told Dennis's mum and dad and Annie what would be best for Dennis and his little sister.

Annie told Dennis and his little sister who would be looking after them and where they would be living. Dennis and his little sister felt happy and sad and also a bit scared. And so the clever Owl asked Annie to go on visiting them and to make sure they were looked after properly.

14

15

Sometimes boys and girls are like Dennis and his little sister.

Sometimes their own mums and dads can't look after them and they have to go and live with other people.

When mums and dads and grown-ups can't decide what is best for boys and girls, they can ask a clever person, called a Judge (like the Owl in the story), to help them. It's the Judge's job to make big decisions about where children should live, whom they should live with and who should visit them.

The Judge will want to know all about the children and their family and will ask someone to find out what they would like to happen. That person will talk to the children and to all the grown-ups who know the children well. The Judge will listen to what everyone has to say before making big decisions.

Sometimes boys and girls have lots of different feelings and worries when big decisions have to be made.

Perhaps big decisions are being made about you and you have some worries. Perhaps you could talk to the grown-ups about your thoughts and feelings, just like Dennis and his little sister did.